I Love You With
All My Hearts... and More

Sally Huss

We sat with our mother under a tree.

It was there that a thought occurred to me.

So I asked, "How much do you love us, Mother dear?"

She said with a smile, "Aaah, let me make it clear.

I love you from the bottom of the ocean

to the top of the sky

And everything in between where the birds fly by."

My brother asked, "Where does this love come from?
Where is it kept?"

"In all of my hearts," our mother quipped.

We were surprised, "You have more hearts than just one?"

"Oh, yes," she said, "I have a ton!"

Then, she began to elaborate

On this most unusual state.

"I have a heart full of love that feeds you day and night

To make sure you grow up strong, straight, and right.

And, I have a heart that keeps you clean…

from your toes to your hair to your teeth so that you beam.

I even have a heart that protects you from dangers

like crossing the street,

Or eating something you shouldn't eat.

I have a heart full of comfort

when your own heart gets broken

By harsh words about you someone may have spoken."

My brother and I had to agree,

"These hearts are big a help to you and me."

Our mother continued, "I have a heart that encourages you to
always do your best,
Whether it's being a good friend…

or taking a test.

I have a heart full of love, this one full of pride,

That I use when you share with another…

or have learned something new that you've tried.

I have another heart that makes sure you know

right from wrong,

Like learning to take turns…

and helping others to get along.

I have another important heart, one full of care.

When you have a disappointment, like losing your kitten,

I'm always there.

I have a heart that supports you when you take a tumble.

As hard as you try, you sometimes still stumble.

I have a heart full of patience as you take your time

to learn something new.

I wait and watch and am proud of you."

We sighed thinking of how wonderful

all of our mother's hearts were.

We now had a greater appreciation of her.

She smiled again, "Yes, there are hearts for every job or task

For which a mother could possibly be asked.

But, as far as I'm concerned it doesn't matter

where one ends or starts –

I love you with all my hearts!"

Then she added something to what she said before,

"Yes, I love you with all my hearts… and more!"

The end,
but not the end
of appreciating
mothers.

How many hearts does your mother have?

A heart that feeds you and keeps you healthy and clean

A heart that protects you from dangers

A heart that comforts you when you are sad

A heart that encourages you to do your best

A heart that is proud of you when you do well

A heart that understands when you make a mistake

A heart that supports you in everything you do

A heart that is full of patience while you learn something new

Just as there are all kinds of hearts, there are all kinds of mothers. There are birthmothers, stepmothers, adoptive mothers, and foster mothers. There are mothers of mothers called grandmothers and mothers of grandmothers called great grandmothers. But, they are all mothers with hearts full of love.

At the end of this book you will find a Certificate of Merit that may be issued to any child who has fulfilled the requirements stated in the Certificate. This fine Certificate will easily fit into a 5"x7" frame, and happily suit any girl or boy who receives it!

Sally writes new books all the time. If you would like to be alerted when one of her new books becomes available or when one of her e-books is offered FREE on Amazon, sign up here: http://www.sallyhuss.com/kids-books.html.

If you liked *I Love You With All My Hearts… and More,* please be kind enough to post a short review for it. Thank you.

Here are a few Sally Huss books you might enjoy. They may be found on Amazon as e-books or in softcover.

About the Author/Illustrator

Sally Huss

"Bright and happy," "light and whimsical" have been the catch phrases attached to the writings and art of Sally Huss for over 30 years. Sweet images dance across all of Sally's creations, whether in the form of children's books, paintings, wallpaper, ceramics, baby bibs, purses, clothing, or her King Features syndicated newspaper panel "Happy Musings."

Sally creates children's books to uplift the lives of children and hopes you will join her in this effort by helping spread her happy messages.

Sally is a graduate of USC with a degree in Fine Art and through the years has had 26 of her own licensed art galleries throughout the world.

This certificate may be cut out, framed, and presented to any child who has earned it.

Certificate of Merit

(Name)

The child named above is awarded this
Certificate of Merit for:
*Appreciating his or her mother
*Helping at home
*Following directions

Date: _____

Presented by: _____

Made in the USA
San Bernardino, CA
14 February 2017